What to do
when you can't
tell the time
or
A brief explanation
of time

By
Steve Chinn

Egon Publishers Ltd
618 Leeds Road, Outwood, Wakefield, WF1 2LT

What to do when you can't tell the time

First published 2009

Egon Publishers Ltd
618 Leeds Road, Outwood
Wakefield WF1 2LT

Tel/FAX: 01924 871697
www.egon.co.uk
information@egon.co.uk

ISBN: 978 1904160 98 4

There are 5 books in this series :-

What to do when you can't tell the time
What to do when you can't add and subtract
What to do when you can't multiply and divide
What to do when you can't do the times tables
What to do when you can't do fractions, decimals and percentages

About this book

"To achieve great things, two things are needed; a plan and not quite enough time."

Leonard Bernstein

I spent over half of my teaching career working with dyslexic learners who were really bright, but had seemingly inexplicable difficulties in learning some aspects of the school curriculum, most notably reading and spelling, but also time.

But dyslexics are not the only learners to have difficulties in certain areas of school and life skills. We all have areas of strength and weakness, but not the same mix. Some talented footballers have great intelligence when it comes to kicking a ball. It doesn't sound a very promising skill, kicking a ball, but if you are really good at it you can make a lot of money and become pretty famous!

My experience has taught me that a lot of children and adults have difficulties in understanding how to 'tell' the time and work out timetables, especially when the timetables use the 24 hour clock.

One of the reasons for the difficulty is that the structure of time is based on a long history that has led to time using key numbers that are no longer part of our regular experience. The ancient Egyptians liked 12 as a base for their numbers, whereas today 10 is the favoured base number in most countries. The ancient Babylonians liked 60.

I feel that we often try to teach time at too complex a level to children when they are too young to deal with all its challenges. Consequently, they fail to learn and understand time and the experience of failure does not help future attempts.

Because I taught students who had some barriers to learning I had to develop teaching skills and strategies to help them get over those barriers. If you teach, whether you are a teacher, tutor or parent, it seems a critical pre-requisite to try to understand how people learn and how they fail to learn and then try to develop explanations that circumvent as many learning barriers as possible.

A lot of the content of this book is about not making the assumption that students take all facts and details in their stride. In fact, it is often the clever learner that notices the anomalies and is then phased by the seemingly irrational structure of time.

The consequence of the influences mentioned above is that this is a slightly different book to the other 'What to do...' books. It has more content devoted to explaining the problems created by the way time is structured as I feel that this is a key reason for peoples' confusion and uncertainties when dealing with time.

'A brief explanation of time' is written for adults who want to help children learn and understand about time and for older students and adults who want to help themselves.

The structure of the book

There are two areas of content that are not directly related to instructions about time. The book includes some quotations about time, partly because they are of interest and sometimes amusing and partly because they show that time is a topic that has always generated much thought and from that good quotations.

The second area is the 'Things to know'. These are a collection of explanations of how aspects of time came to be, so that the seemingly illogical or confusing structure of time becomes less threatening.

There are other sections that address some of the issues that may confuse and handicap the learning process. We try to use what we know to understand what we are learning. We expect logical links to new work. If the links are perceived to be illogical then learning becomes less about understanding and more about remembering.

The structure is developmental:

- The key numbers of time
- Circular number lines and clock faces
- Days and hours
- Hours and minutes
- Telling the time
- Times past the hour and times to the hour
- Seconds
- The 24 hour clock
- Months, weeks and days
- Calculations with time

Time

"The only reason for time is so that everything doesn't happen at once."

Albert Einstein

Some things which make time difficult to learn

When we meet a new learning challenge, or a new experience, we often try to relate it to previously learned knowledge or previous experiences. This puts things in a familiar framework and that gives us some security. If the new knowledge or experience does not link to existing knowledge and previous experience, then we become anxious, less effective in our capacity to learn and possibly develop a resistance to being involved with the new work. Any early experience of failure will only confirm our attitude.

Time is a challenge. It is a challenge because it does not obviously link to our past experience and knowledge of numbers and arithmetic. It requires us to adapt to using numbers in ways that are significantly different to our previous experiences. If we can understand those developments and extensions to previous knowledge then time can be mastered.

Four of the main learning challenges of time are:

1. Until we meet time our experience of numbers is based on units, tens, hundreds, thousands (1, 10, 100, 1000, and upwards) for as long as we wish to count. Time is based on 1, 12, 24 and 60.

2. We usually meet numbers in straight lines. When we write 1 to 12 we write in a line:

   1 2 3 4 5 6 7 8 9 10 11 12

   The analogue clock face presents the numbers in a circle.

Traditional analogue clock face

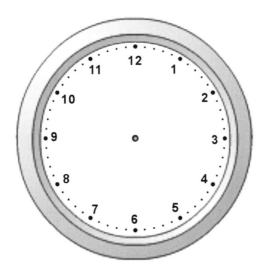

3. We use the same circular number line to represent three different measures of time: hours, minutes and seconds.

4. In time we use counting down as well as counting up. When time passes the half hour (30 minutes), we start to count down to the next hour, for example we say 'twenty three minutes to seven', then 'twenty-two minutes to seven', then twenty-one minutes to seven' and so on.

There are other difficulties to address which this book will explain later.

The key numbers of time

Time works with different key numbers than the ones we normally use. For time 12, 24 and 60 are the key numbers, but for everyday arithmetic 10, 100 and 1000 are the key numbers.

So, for time there are:

- 24 hours in 1 day
- 12 hours for am (midnight to midday)
- 12 hours for pm (midday to midnight)
- There are 60 minutes in 1 hour
- And 60 seconds in a minute

"Day: A period of 24 hours, mostly misspent."
Ambrose Brierce

"The future is something which everyone reaches
at the rate of sixty minutes an hour,
whatever he does, whoever he is."
C S Lewis

Some examples of everyday arithmetic values

These are based on 10 and powers of ten,
(100, 1000, 10,000 and so on).

Examples are:

- 100 pence in one pound (100p in £1)
- 10 millimetres in 1 centimetre
- 100 centimetres in 1 metre
- 1000 grams in 1 kilogram
- 1000 metres in a kilometre
- 100 years in a century
- £1,000,000 is a million pounds

Clocks and watches - numbers in a circle

A digital clock (or watch) simply shows the digits for a particular time at that particular time, for example:

An analogue clock face has a circular number line, that is, the numbers are arranged in a circle. Whereas when we measure length with a ruler, the ruler is straight.

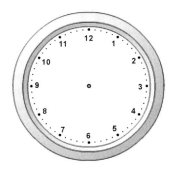

The circular number line on an analogue clock face, which has numbers up to 12, is used twice in a day for measuring hours since a day has 24 hours (12 x 2).

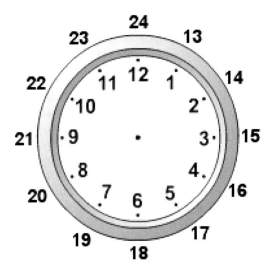

No matter what length of time we measure, a clock face only needs 12 numbers. A clock has a circular, repeating, number line.

9

Why is 12 at the top?

The historical reason why 12 is placed at the top of the clock face is because that was the central place for 12 noon on a sundial.

The number line on a clock face is even more challenging to past experience, because one number line is used to represent three quantities, hours, minutes and seconds.

This is even more confusing because the only numbers (usually) given on the scale are for the hours. In order to help us distinguish between which of the three scales to use an analogue clock has three pointers, called 'hands'.

One, the smallest, is for hours. The next hand, longer, is for minutes. The third hand, sometimes in a different colour, and the fastest moving hand, is for seconds.

So, it is not the scales that are different, it is the hands.

There is a potential for language confusion with the names used for the hands on a clock.

The fast hand is used for seconds, even though it might be considered to be the third hand!! Unfortunately, in the English language we use 'second' with two meanings: being between first and third place, and as 1/60 of a minute. The name 'second' hand is nothing to do with any arbitrary order of ranking the hands. It may help to know why these names are used. (Also 'second hand' has another meaning as seen, for example, in charity shops).

Why minutes and seconds?

The history behind these names helps to explain their particular logic.

The minute hand of a clock was so called because it represented smaller (mi-nute) units of time (than hours).

The second hand was so called because it represented a secondary level of mi-nuteness of time.

So, minutes are small or mi-nute and seconds are even smaller or at a secondary level of smallness.

The basic quantities of time - days and hours

There are 24 hours in a day. Under normal circumstances we work in terms of using 12 hours twice, using **am** to identify morning for the first 12 hours and **pm** to mean afternoon and evening for the second 12 hours.

What was wrong with night-time?

Back in deepest history, only daytime was divided into 12 parts. Night-time was just night-time. Maybe if you were asleep that made sense?

To distinguish between daytime and nightime we use 'am' and 'pm'. This is a way to recognise and label which of the two twelve hours we are using. From midnight to midday we use 'am' after the numbers to identify that it is morning.
For example, 10:00 am is ten o'clock in the morning. And from midday to midnight we use 'pm' to identify that it is afternoon or evening. For example, 9:00 pm is nine o'clock in the evening. So we might eat breakfast at 7am, and later we might eat supper at 8pm.

Why am and pm?

- am is short for 'ante meridiem' which means 'before midday'

- pm is short for 'post meridiem' which means 'after midday'

So midday is the focus time.

If we used a straight number line to represent the 24 hours of one day, then, as for the circular number line, the first 12 hours are labelled 'am' and the second 12 hours are labelled 'pm'.

am and pm are centred on Midday

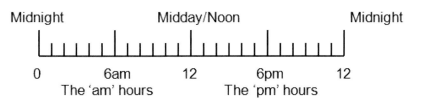

So, if I just said '8 o'clock' you would not know if that was 8 in the morning or 8 in the evening. By using 'am' and 'pm' you can tell which 8 o'clock I mean.

Why 'clock' and 'o'clock' ?

O'clock is a shortened version of 'of the clock', which is how time was spoken centuries ago: 'Eight of the clock'. Clock comes from the Latin word for bell, 'clocca'. The first clocks, about 700 years ago, were bells that were rung to tell people the time and/or to call them to prayer.

Why 12 hours?

The ancient Egyptians were the first to divide the day into 12 hours. They used a sundial for measuring time, so as the length of the day changed according to the time of year, the length of an hour changed. In fact hours did not become a consistent quantity until the fourteenth century, around 2000 years later.

For a while it was thought that night and daytime were different in terms of time, partly because there is no sun at night for the sundial. Eventually the Egyptians decided to give both night and daytime 12 hours, making 24 hours in a whole day.

The number 12 was chosen because we have twelve sections, three on each of the four fingers of one hand (the thumb was used to count them).

Clocks and hours

The hour hand moves at a very slow but steady speed around the clock. It does not jump from one hour to the next. As time gets closer to the next hour the hour hand gets closer to the next number on the clock face.

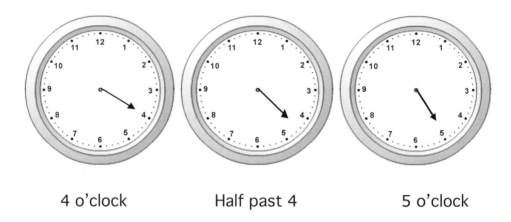

4 o'clock   Half past 4   5 o'clock

If we wanted to gauge a time that fell between the hours we could look at the position of the hour hand as it moved from one hour to the next hour. So if we had a clock with only an hour hand we may be able to judge when it was half way past an hour, or maybe even quarter and three quarters past an hour.

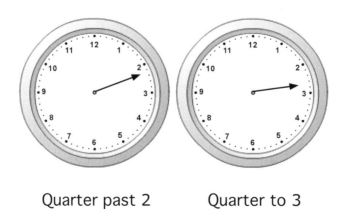

Quarter past 2   Quarter to 3

Why 'hands'?

Judging parts of an hour would have been like the situation above for the first clock faces. There was just one pointer shaped like a hand and a moving dial/face.

Clocks and fractions - adding more accuracy to times

We can be more accurate in judging the time between hours by using the minute hand. There are some key values based on what fraction of the circle the minute hand has moved.

Memories of 'doing fractions' at school are rarely good. However, the fractions used in time are restricted to the two values most of us can understand, half, ½, and quarter, ¼. Hopefully this familiarity will remove any anxiety.

An hour can be divided into halves (30 minutes out of 60 minutes) and quarters (15 minutes out of 60 minutes).

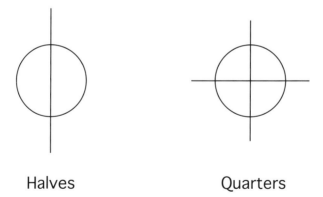

Halves   Quarters

The use of these two fractions means we can be more precise in stating a time than if we were restricted to hours alone.

For example, if we take 11pm as our example we can now add in:

Quarter (of an hour) past eleven   11:15 pm
Half (of an hour) past eleven   11:30 pm
Quarter (of an hour) to twelve   11:45 pm

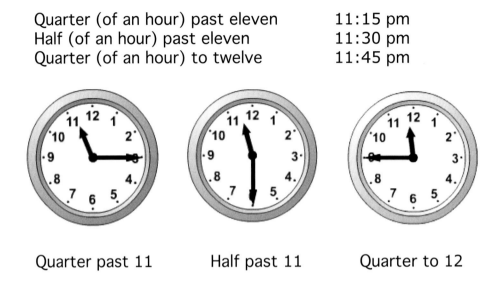

Quarter past 11   Half past 11   Quarter to 12

Note: we do not use the sequence, quarter past, half past and three quarters past. We take the three quarters past and visualise it in terms of the quarter left before the next hour. The sequence becomes, quarter past, half past and quarter to.

Summary and practice

O'clock

The minute hand (the big hand) points exactly to 12.

The hour hand (the small hand) points exactly to the number representing the hour.

In the example below, the time is 'four o'clock'.

Half past the hour

The minute hand (the big hand) points exactly to 6 (half way around the clock).

The hour hand (the small hand) has moved half way towards the next number (hour).

You read the o'clock hour that has just past and use 'half past ..... '

In the example below, the time is 'half past three'.

Quarter past the hour

The minute hand (the big hand) points exactly to 3 (quarter the way around the clock).

The hour hand (the small hand) has moved to a quarter of the way towards the next number (hour).

You read the o'clock hour that has just past and use 'quarter past ....'

In the example below the time is 'quarter past ten'.

Quarter to the hour

The big hand (the minute hand) points exactly to 9 (one quarter away from going all around the clock).

The small hand (the hour hand) has moved three quarters the way towards the next number (hour).

You read the hour that is next and use 'quarter to ....'
In the example below the time is 'quarter to seven'.

Practice: o'clock times

1.

2.

3.

4.

5.

6.

Answers:

1)....................... 2)....................... 3).......................

4)....................... 5)....................... 6).......................

Practice: half past times

1.

2.

3.

4.

5.

6.

Answers:

1)....................... 2)....................... 3).......................

4)....................... 5)....................... 6).......................

Practice: quarter past times

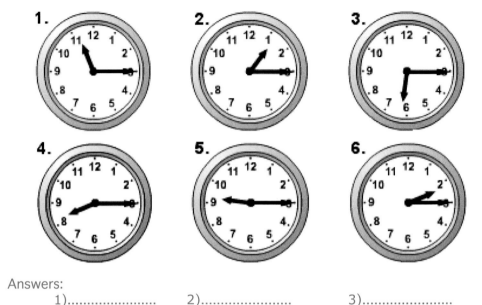

Answers:

1).....................   2).....................   3).....................

4).....................   5).....................   6).....................

Practice: quarter to times

Answers:

1).....................   2).....................   3).....................

4).....................   5).....................   6).....................

More practice

Draw hands on these blank clocks to match the times written underneath.

(Don't forget that the hour hand moves steadily between hours).

1. Seven o'clock   2. Half past two   3. Quarter past 9

4. Quarter to three   5. Ten o'clock   6. Half past four

7. Quarter past twelve   8. Quarter to one   9. Half past six

Why a circular clock face?

Time goes on forever, but in cycles. The Earth goes round the Sun once a year. The Moon goes round the Earth once every 28 days. Each day has the same cycle of 24 hours. The year, the month and the day come round at their own fixed period of time. Time has a cyclic character. So, for example, every day has a 9:30 am or a 7:00 pm. Every day has its own am and pm times which are the same times as any other day. The cyclic nature of time results in a circular time line on a clock face.

An advantage for the analogue clock

One of the advantages of an analogue clock over a digital clock is that the clock face shows all twelve hours so that the current time is always set in context of the whole clock face. For example, when an analogue clock reads 9:45am there is visual support to estimate how long it is until midday. When a digital clock displays 9:45 that is the limit of the information it provides. Any attempt to put 9:45 in the context of midday requires a numerical calculation based on an understanding of time.

Roman numerals

Some analogue clocks use Roman numerals. These are very straightforward to understand. The visual position of the numerals may be all you need to 'read' the time.

You can work out any number using just 7 Roman numerals:

I = 1	V = 5	X = 10
L = 50	C = 100	D = 500 M = 1000

They used the shortest number of letters to get to the number required.

So to make the numbers on a clockface it would look like this:

I = 1   II = 2   III = 3   IV = 4 (note: the 1 before 5)
V = 5   VI = 6 (5 + 1)   VII = 7   VIII = 8
IX = 9 (i.e. 1 before 10)   X = 10   XI = 11 (i.e. 10 + 1)   XII = 12

N.B. The key is to add the numbers together if the larger one appears first; but subtract the number if the larger number appears second.

They are also used to write a year, particularly for films or important documents. Once we got to the millennium the length of the date was much easier to read:
1999 was MCMXCIX   whereas 2000 was MM   2016 is MXVI

Close enough for government work

I worked with a young student in the USA, trying to improve his maths skills. He would work out an answer, which was often very close to the 'correct' answer, but not always accurate. He would shrug his shoulders, smile and say, "close enough for government work." Being precisely correct did not motivate him. Being 'close enough' was fine and he was not going to get stressed by any requirement to get a 'right' answer.

If you can master time in terms of the quarters and the half hour, then you can get close enough most of the time.

Eight o'clock	Just after 8 o'clock
Heading up to quarter past 8	Quarter past 8
After quarter past 8	Almost half past 8
Half past 8	Just after half past 8
Coming up to quarter to 9	Quarter to 9
Just after quarter to 9	Close to 9 o'clock
9 o'clock	

These thirteen phrases give 8 approximate times and 5 accurate times for each hour. That's close enough for a lot of the time.

Write your timetable for your day:

Wake up   _____ am

Breakfast   _____ am

Off to school or work   _____ am

Lunch   _____ pm

Back home   _____ pm

Supper   _____ pm

Bed time   _____ pm

"A good holiday is one spent among people
whose notions of time are vaguer than yours."
John B. Priestley

The basic quantities of time - hours and minutes

Adding more accuracy to times

There are 24 hours in a day. We can break down the time in a day into 24 hours.

Time can be measured just in hours, but if we want to be more precise, then we need minutes as well as hours. Quarter and half hours may not be precise enough for all occasions.

There are 60 minutes in an hour. We can break down the time in an hour into 60 minutes.

If we take a 12 hour time line, each hour is divided up into 60 minutes.

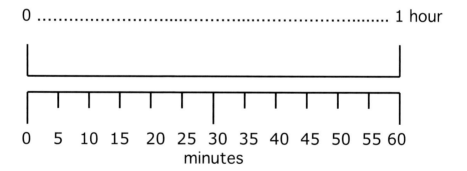

Time line for 1 hour / 60 minutes

The increased accuracy of having minutes on a clock could only happen when the technology made it possible. If a burning candle was used to measure time, then division of an hour into 60 small, minute (mi-nute) parts was not possible. The invention of the pendulum clock made minutes a realistic and accurate proposition.

Why 60 minutes in an hour?

The answer is 4000 years old. The ancient Babylonians liked 60. It was the lowest number that was divisible by all of the first six numbers, 1, 2, 3, 4, 5 and 6, so maybe that persuaded them it was a good number to use.

How many minutes in a day?

There are 24 hours in a day and each hour has 60 minutes, so the number of minutes in a day is 1440.

$$24 \times 60 = 1440 \text{ minutes}$$

How many minutes in a year?

There are 365 days in a year and each day has 1440 minutes, so the number of minutes in a year is 525,600.

$$365 \times 1440 = 525,600 \text{ minutes}$$

(This is over half a million minutes).

Clock faces and minutes

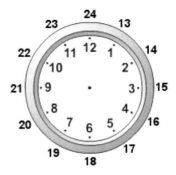

A clock face has a circular number line for 12 hours. The hour circular number line is used twice in a day, once for am times and once for pm times. The clock face above shows the hours for the 24 hour clock.

The circular number line has three uses:

- am hours
- pm hours
- minutes

It has a fourth use if the clock or watch has a hand for seconds.

In order to measure the 60 minutes in an hour, each of the 12 intervals in the number line are divided up into 5 smaller intervals, making 60 marks in all.

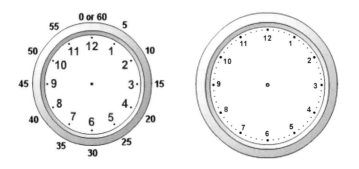

So that we can tell when we are using the minute intervals and when we are using the hour intervals, we have two different pointers. Pointers on a clock are called 'hands'.

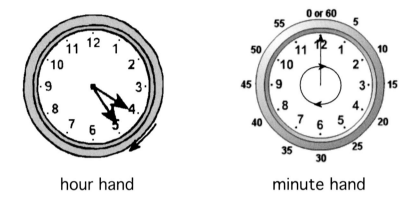

hour hand   minute hand

One pointer or hand is used for the hour intervals and the other pointer or hand is used for the minutes.

So that you can tell which hand is for hours and which is for minutes, one is shorter than the other.

The hour hand is shorter than the minute hand.

It should be obvious that the minute hand will move faster than the hour hand.

While the hour hand moves through a one hour interval on the circular number line, the minute hand moves through 60 minute intervals.

28

In order for this to make sense, you have to remember that the two number lines, the one for hours and the one for minutes, are really quite different even though, in a sense, they have been blended into one line. They represent different number values.

The straight lines below shows the comparisons between hour values and minute values.

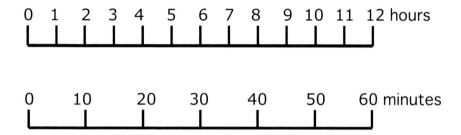

The clock face overleaf illustrates what happens to the hands in one hour. From 3 pm to 4 pm, 3 o'clock to 4 o'clock, the hour hand moves 1 hour interval. In that same I hour interval, the minute hand moves round the complete circle.

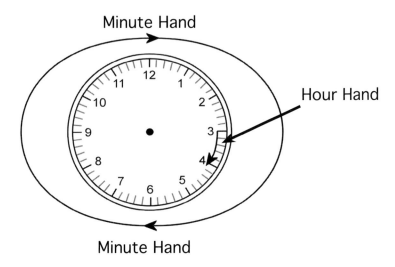

Because the clock time lines share the same circle, but have different scales, the minute hand moves faster, 12 times faster than the hour hand.

Why 'hands'?

When clock faces or dials were first introduced, around 600 years ago, the dial moved and the time was marked by a fixed pointer, which was often shaped like a hand.

> *"The clock has decided to take time into its own hands."*
>
> *Anon*

Why is clockwise left to right (starting from 12)?

In the Northern hemisphere of the world, that is the way the shadow on a sundial moves. The clock face was invented in the Northern hemisphere and was influenced by the sundial in the direction for the hands and in having 12 at the top of the face.

And, if a clock is fixed to a wall, the minute hand effectively moves down until it reaches 30 minutes. After this, it effectively moves up.

Counting on (after) and counting up (before)

Another aspect of time that is unusual, or different to previous experience with numbers, is that when we count the 60 minutes between one hour and the next we count on until we get half way (30) and then we often change to counting down to the next hour, 29, 28, 27, 26.... (There is a potential for confusion here, as the minute hand moves up the clock face, the numbers left to reach the next hour count down).

So, we have two choices of how we 'say' time after any half hour, after 30 minutes. For example, if we start at 8:30 (it could be am or pm, so we shall use neither!)

Choice 1: We carry on counting up numerically, so that 1 minute after 8:30 we say 8:31.

This pattern continues: 8:31, 8:32, 8:33, 8:34 ...

Until: ... 8:57, 8:58, 8:59 then 9:00, 9 o'clock.

Choice 2: We pass the half way point and, instead of counting on from 8:30 we start to count down to 9:00, the next hour.

At 8:30, we have 30 minutes left to reach 9:00. So, after 1 minute there are 29 minutes left until 9:00, 'twenty nine to nine', then

28 minutes to 9:00, 27 minutes to 9:00, 26 minutes to 9:00.

This pattern continues, getting ever closer to 9:00:

3 minutes to 9:00, 2 minutes to 9:00, 1 minute to 9:00, 9 o'clock.

31

As the minute **hand** moves **up**, we count **down** the numbers for the minutes left until the next hour.

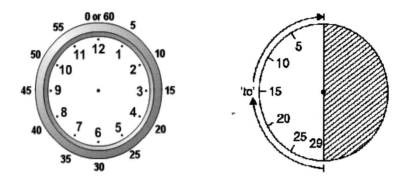

Reminder: counting down is used for the quarter hours, as well.

For 3:45 we almost always 'count down' to the next hour, so we say 'quarter to four' rather than 'three quarters past three'.

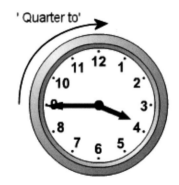

Examples of 'minutes past the hour'

Sixteen minutes past 11   Six minutes past 2   Seventeen minutes past 9

Examples of 'minutes to the hour'

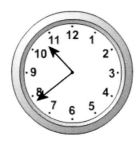

Seven minutes to 3   Twenty-two minutes to 11   Seventeen minutes to 2

By using the 60 minutes we can 'tell' the time quite precisely. This level of precision is sufficient for many needs, such as train times, television programme times, shop closing times, cinema times or school timetables.

Minutes are not decimals

There are a couple more potential misconceptions about times.

In this book I have used a colon   :   to separate hours and minutes, so a time is presented as, for example, 6:30.

In some everyday representations you will also see times written with a single dot as in 6.30. It is important NOT to confuse this dot with a decimal point.

So 6:50 pm is NOT 6 and a half hours. It is 'six fifty' or 'ten to seven'. Whereas $6.50 is six and a half dollars.

And 6.30 pm is not 6 and 3 tenths of an hour nor is it 6 and 30 hundredths of an hour. 6.30 pm is 6 and 30 sixtieths, 30/60, which is 6 and a half hours.

The quarter in context

In the USA, where the 'quarter', 25 cents, is a very common and popular coin, students sometimes confuse 'quarters' from money across to time and write 3:25 for a 'quarter past 3'.

A quarter in time is a quarter of 60 minutes (15). But a 'quarter' for money in the USA means a quarter of 100 cents (25).

Both these examples are about the context in which a symbol or a word is used. The same symbol or word can have a very different meaning in one maths area than it does in another maths area or have a different meaning in a maths sense than in an everyday sense, for example 'take away' can mean subtraction or food.

Some timetables, for example the timetable for trains in my area, do not use any symbol to separate hours and minutes, so 20:37 is printed as 2037.

This is another example of context. We know it is a timetable and that the numbers are representing time. The designers of the timetable assume that we can generalise and recognise that for the four digits, the first two mean hours and the second two mean minutes.

This four-digit style introduces a need to deal with times that are single digit for hours, that is up to and including 9, for example, 7:18 am.

To keep the representation consistently at four digits a zero is introduced, for example, 7:18 am becomes 0718.

The introduction of the zero is, once again, a new experience for learners. We do not put zeros in front of whole numbers in everyday arithmetic.

Seconds - even more accuracy

A minute can be split into 60 seconds.

We may not always use this level of accuracy, for example, it would be unrealistically optimistic to expect a British train to arrive at the precision of seconds. So, even though we have the opportunity to deal in this level of accuracy, we may not always make use of it.

We tend to make the most use of seconds when we are dealing with short time intervals, such as 20 seconds or 90 seconds, rather than when we are using times that run into hours.

For some athletic events such as the 100 metres, race times are measured to one hundredth of a second!

How many seconds in one hour?

There are 60 minutes in one hour and there are 60 seconds in each minute. So the number of seconds in one hour is:

$$1 \text{ hour } = 60 \times 60 = 3600 \text{ seconds}$$

A sobering fact

A car travelling at only 30 miles per hour covers 44 feet in one second (almost 15 yards).

Or in metric units:

A car travelling at only 50 kilometres per hour covers almost 14 metres in one second.

(You can do the maths for other speeds, for example, at 60mph the distance covered is twice that at 30mph, almost 30 yards or 28 metres.)

Are all minutes 60 seconds?

Atomic clocks are super-accurate. In fact they are so accurate that in order to keep atomic time in line with astronomical time a leap second is added about once a year. So, not all minutes contain 60 seconds. About once every year one minute contains one extra second, making it a 61 second minute.

Time and language

When we learn anything new we tend to look for patterns and for consistency.

Unfortunately there are some exceptions and inconsistencies in the language of time that can lead to confusion.

For example, we say 'ten past six' and we write 6:10 (though we do sometimes say 'six ten').

And, even more confusingly, we say 'ten to nine' and write 8:50.

We say 'quarter past eight' and write 8:15.

We say 'quarter to ten' and write 9:45.

There is a pattern, but it is not always the obvious, previously experienced, straightforward translation of words to numbers.

We need to practise writing the different ways we say times such as 6:10 and 8:50 and the way we write times such as 'ten past six' and 'ten to nine'.

Practice

Example: Write 'ten to nine' ('ten minutes to nine hours') in numbers:

Answer: 8:50

Now try these examples, and write the 'am' times in numbers:

a) Twenty past seven   ....

b) Half past three   ....

c) Four forty   ....

d) Quarter to five   ....

e) Five past nine   ....

f) Five to eleven   ....

Answers:

a) 7:20 am b) 3:30 am c) 4:40 am d) 4:45 am e)9:05am f)10:55 am

Some different examples

Write these times as 'minutes to hour'.

Answer: 7:50 is 'ten to eight'.

Try these examples:

a) 06:55   ....

b) 10:40   ....

c) 02:35   ....

d) 01:45   ....

e) 01:48   ....

f) 11:38   ....

Answers:

a) Five minutes to seven b) Twenty to eleven c) Twenty-five to three d) Quarter to two e) Twenty-two minutes to two f) Twelve minutes to twelve

The 24 hour clock

Times may be given in terms of the 24 hour clock. This tends to happen mostly for travel timetables, such as trains and planes.

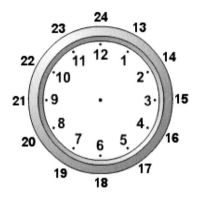

Instead of dividing the 24 hours in a day into two equal parts of 12 hours, and using am and pm to distinguish which 12 is being used, the 24 hour clock sets all times of a day consecutively in numbers up to 24, that is, not repeating at 12.

This means that 1:00 pm, which is the next hour after 12:00 noon, becomes 13:00.

1:00 pm becomes 13:00   (12 + 1 = 13)

and 8:00 pm becomes 20:00   (12 + 8 = 20)

With the 24 hour clock, there is no need for 'am' and 'pm'. **'am'** hours are the hours from midnight to noon and are 00:00 to 12:00. **'pm'** hours are the hours from noon to midnight and are 12:00 to 24:00. So, by using the 24 hour clock, am and pm are made redundant.

Times from midnight will cover after 00:00 to 11:59 and then 12:00. Times from midday will cover after 12:00 to 23:59 and then 00:00.

This can be illustrated in a linear time line.

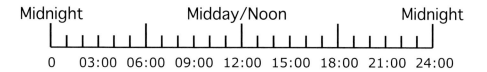

Calculating 4:30 pm in 24 hour time

Starting from midnight there are 12 hours in the morning (up to midday) and then a further 4:30 hours in the afternoon, which we add together to get the 24 hour time:

$$12 + 4:30 = 16:30$$

Midnight   Midday/Noon   Midnight

0 03:00   06:00 09:00 12:00 15:00 18:00 21:00 24:00

$$12:00 + 4:30 = 16:30$$

To convert from pm time to 24 hour time

The procedure is: Cross out 'pm' and add 12

For example:

3:30 pm > cross out pm > 3:30 > add 12 > 15:30

10:15 pm > cross out pm > 10:15 > add 12 > 22:15

Practice

Convert these pm times to 24 hour clock times.

a) 4:15 pm   ....

b) 7:30 pm   ....

c) 5:50 pm   ....

d) 8:07 pm   ....

e) 9:42 pm   ....

f) 10:14 pm   ....

g) 11.55 pm   ....

Answers

a) 16:15   b) 19:30   c) 17:50   d) 20:07   e) 21:42   f) 22:14   g) 23:55

To convert from 24 hour time to pm time

Do the reverse procedure.   (Take away 12 and write 'pm'.)

For example:

16:30 > take away 12 > 4:30 > add pm > 4:30pm

and

23:15 > take away 12 > 11:15 > add pm > 11:15pm

Practice

Convert these 24 hour clock times to pm times.

a) 14:15   ....

b) 17:22   ....

c) 19:05   ....

d) 15:43   ....

e) 20:25   ....

f) 21:30   ....

g) 23:47   ....

Answers

e) 8:25 pm   f) 9:30 pm   g) 11:47 pm

a) 2:15 pm   b) 5:22 pm   c) 7:05 pm   d) 3:43 pm

Another potential language confusion

When a 24 hour time is on the hour, for example,

11 o'clock (am) may be spoken as 'Eleven hundred hours' and written 11:00.

7 o'clock (am) may be spoken as 'O seven hundred hours' and written 07:00.

Bizarrely 'hundred' is used even though there are 60 minutes in an hour.

Analogue and digital clocks

For many people the choice between buying a digital watch or an analogue watch is a matter of which they prefer based on the appearance or design. A digital watch or clock has an advantage in that it shows the time in a way that you can read out directly

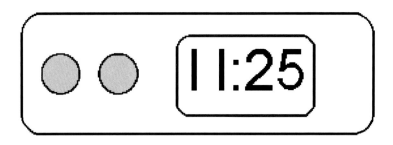

My bedside clock showing 11:25

I prefer a digital bedside clock because I can still read the time even when I am half asleep! But in my waking hours I prefer an analogue watch because it gives me a better concept of time gone and time to come as I plan my days.

Time is not just about knowing what the time is now. A digital clock will tell you what the time is right now. It doesn't give any visual clues as to where that time fits into the hour or the day. Sometimes you need to know, probably via a visual estimate how much time has elapsed since an event or how much time is left before an event. Understanding and managing time can make life and work more efficient and even less stressful.

An analogue clock divides the 12 hour, 60 minute clock face visually so that, by proportion you can 'see' where the current time is in relation to the hour or the (half) day.

For example, if the minute hand is showing 15 minutes, quarter past the hour, the visual appearance shows that there is three quarters of an hour left until the next hour.

We can easily visualise a half and a quarter of a clock face.

The basic quantities of time - months and days

Learning the months of the year

> *"My doctor gave me six months to live, but when*
> *I couldn't pay the bill he gave me six months more."*
>
> *Walter Matthau*

2 0 1 4

January						
Mo	Tu	We	Th	Fr	Sa	Su
		1	2	3	4	5
6	7	8	9	10	11	12
13	14	15	16	17	18	19
20	21	22	23	24	25	26
27	28	29	30	31		

February						
Mo	Tu	We	Th	Fr	Sa	Su
					1	2
3	4	5	6	7	8	9
10	11	12	13	14	15	16
17	18	19	20	21	22	23
24	25	26	27	28		

March						
Mo	Tu	We	Th	Fr	Sa	Su
31					1	2
3	4	5	6	7	8	9
10	11	12	13	14	15	16
17	18	19	20	21	22	23
24	25	26	27	28	29	30

April						
Mo	Tu	We	Th	Fr	Sa	Su
	1	2	3	4	5	6
7	8	9	10	11	12	13
14	15	16	17	18	19	20
21	22	23	24	25	26	27
28	29	30				

May						
Mo	Tu	We	Th	Fr	Sa	Su
			1	2	3	4
5	6	7	8	9	10	11
12	13	14	15	16	17	18
19	20	21	22	23	24	25
26	27	28	29	30	31	

June						
Mo	Tu	We	Th	Fr	Sa	Su
30						1
2	3	4	5	6	7	8
9	10	11	12	13	14	15
16	17	18	19	20	21	22
23	24	25	26	27	28	29

July						
Mo	Tu	We	Th	Fr	Sa	Su
	1	2	3	4	5	6
7	8	9	10	11	12	13
14	15	16	17	18	19	20
21	22	23	24	25	26	27
28	29	30	31			

August						
Mo	Tu	We	Th	Fr	Sa	Su
				1	2	3
4	5	6	7	8	9	10
11	12	13	14	15	16	17
18	19	20	21	22	23	24
25	26	27	28	29	30	31

September						
Mo	Tu	We	Th	Fr	Sa	Su
1	2	3	4	5	6	7
8	9	10	11	12	13	14
15	16	17	18	19	20	21
22	23	24	25	26	27	28
29	30					

October						
Mo	Tu	We	Th	Fr	Sa	Su
		1	2	3	4	5
6	7	8	9	10	11	12
13	14	15	16	17	18	19
20	21	22	23	24	25	26
27	28	29	30	31		

November						
Mo	Tu	We	Th	Fr	Sa	Su
					1	2
3	4	5	6	7	8	9
10	11	12	13	14	15	16
17	18	19	20	21	22	23
24	25	26	27	28	29	30

December						
Mo	Tu	We	Th	Fr	Sa	Su
1	2	3	4	5	6	7
8	9	10	11	12	13	14
15	16	17	18	19	20	21
22	23	24	25	26	27	28
29	30	31				

In order to succeed in this task you have to do two things:

- learn the names of the twelve months
- get them in the right order

There is a rote learning technique that can be very effective. However, even this powerful technique won't work for everybody. The only way to find out if it works for you is to give it a try. If it works, it usually works quickly.

The technique is:

Write out the months, clustered into four groups of three months (you may need to experiment with groups as you may succeed better with groups of 2 or 4 or 6 months).

Record the information, in your own voice, onto a computer or audio recorder, in the chunks that work for you (2, 3, 4 or 6).

Put on headphones and play back a chunk of months while looking at them on screen or paper.

Repeat the playback of the same months several times.

You may find that you are muttering the words, sub-vocalising them. This can be a powerful aid to memorising information.

Move onto the next chunk of months.

If this works then practise all 12 months at one time using the same technique.

(This method was pioneered by Dr Colin Lane. Search for 'self-voice echo' to find out more.)

> *"I've been on a calendar, but I have never been on time."*
>
> *Marilyn Monroe*

Why are there 12 months in a year?

Again we have to blame the Babylonians of 4000 years ago. They calculated that a year had 360 days and divided it up into 12 months. One possible reason for choosing 12 is that a hand has four fingers and each finger has three sections (separated by 2 joints). They could use the thumb to do the counting of the joints on the four fingers. If we based the months on the number of lunar (moon) cycles in a year, then we would have 13 months.

Months, weeks and days

There are 12 months in a year.

There are 52 weeks in a year.

A 'quarter' of a year is 13 weeks.

There are 365 days in a year and 366 days in a Leap Year.

Every fourth year is a Leap Year (2012, the year of the London Olympics was a leap year).

All months do not have the same (total) number of days:

28 days: February   (29 in a Leap Year)

30 days: April   June   September   November

31 days: January   March   May   July
August   October   December

Things to know - clock faces and angles

If you like angles, it might help you to know that a clock face, being a full circle covers 360°.

This means that half a circle is 180°

A quarter circle is 90°

The hours divide the circle into twelve 30° segments.

 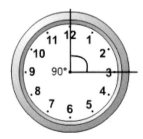 

Adding with time - hours

An example would be:

A journey starts at 3 pm and takes 6 hours.
When do you arrive?

6 hours can be added directly to 3 pm

3 pm + 6 hours = 9 pm

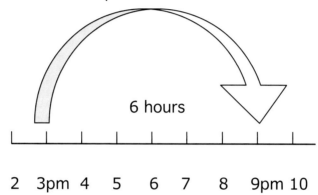

6 hours

2   3pm 4   5   6   7   8   9pm 10

An example which takes us across the 12 (whether midday or midnight) requires an extra step:

A journey starts at 10:00 am and takes 6 hours.
At what pm time do you arrive?

Working from previous knowledge of numbers and arithmetic this becomes

10 + 6   (= 16)

BUT hours do not work on our normal number base of 10. Hours work on a number base of 12. If we work in am and pm time then the calculation takes two steps.

Crossing 12 makes the calculation slightly (I hope only slightly) more difficult. But, if you know that 12 midday has to be crossed, then it becomes possible to get the right answer.

If we took a clock face and made it into a straight number line, it would look like this:

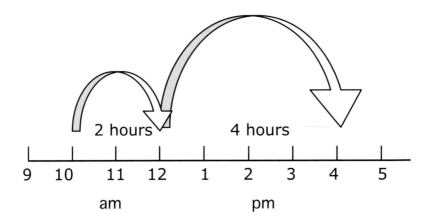

The change from am time to pm time happens at 12:00 (midday/noon), so we have to start at 10:00 and aim for 12:00. This takes the first 2 hours of the journey. This is represented by the first arc.

There are 4 hours left to travel (6 – 2 = 4). The second arc takes us to 4:00pm.

If we work with 24 hour time, then the calculation can be done in one step, because we do not cross the 24:

$$10:00 + 6 = 16:00$$

Two examples using the 24 hour clock:

> A plane takes off at 05:00 hours and lands 10 hours later. At what time does it land?
> (Give your answer as 24 hour clock time).

$$05:00 + 10 = 15:00$$

The time does not cross 24, so the addition is straightforward.

A plane takes off at 22:00 and lands 5 hours later.
At what time does it land?

In the 24 hour version of the second example, the time crosses 24 hrs. We have to remember that numbers for time change when they cross 24. So, this problem is similar in principle to those that cross the 12.

This can be shown with a 24 hour time line:

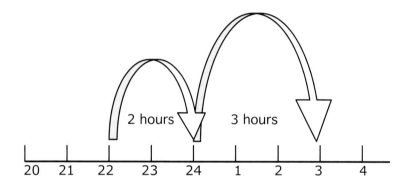

The first 2 hours of the journey take us to the key time of 24:00 hours. There are 3 hours left to travel:

$$5 - 2 = 3$$

Those 3 hours take us to 03:00 hours

When adding time, you have to remember the importance of these facts:

am and pm time work on 12 hour cycles

the 24 hour clock works on a 24 hour cycle.

Subtracting with time - hours

The procedures for subtraction are the reverse of the procedures used for addition.

Once again, we have to remember the key numbers for hours are 12 and 24.

First example:

A journey ending at 9 pm took 6 hours.
When did you set off?

6 hours can be subtracted directly from 9 pm:

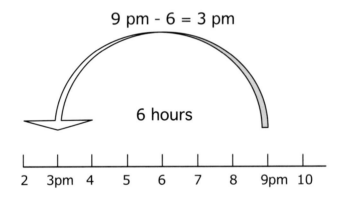

9 pm - 6 = 3 pm

6 hours

2   3pm   4   5   6   7   8   9pm   10

An example which takes us across the 12 requires an extra step:

A journey ends at 4pm and took 6 hours. When did you start? Give your answer in am/pm time.

Using standard number or arithmetic rules creates a problem when your write this out, 4 – 6 = ? as hours do not work in the usual number base of 10. Hours work on a number base of 12.

If we work in am and pm time then the calculation takes two steps.

Crossing 12:00 makes the calculation slightly (again, I hope only slightly) more difficult. But, if you know that 12:00 has to be crossed, then it becomes possible to get right answers.

If we took a clock face and made it into a straight number line, it would look like this:

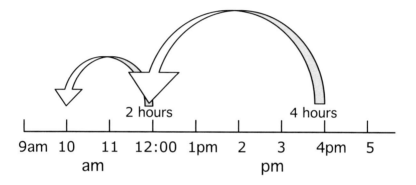

The change from am time to pm time happens at 12:00 (midday/noon), so we have to start the calculation at 4pm and aim back for 12:00. This was the last 4 hours of the journey. This is represented by the bigger arc.

There are 2 hours of the journey left (6 – 4 = 2). The smaller arc takes us back to the start time of 10:00am.

If we work with 24 hour time, then the calculation can be done in one step, because we do not cross the 24. The end of the journey was 4pm or 16:00:

$$16:00 - 6 = 10:00$$

Two more 24 hour examples:

A plane lands at 15:00 hours after a 10 hour flight.
At what time did it take off?

$$15:00 - 10 = 05:00$$

The time does not cross 24, so the subtraction is straightforward.

A plane lands at 03:00 after a 5 hour flight.
At what time did it take off?

In this 24 hour clock version of the second example, the time crosses 24. We have to remember that numbers for time change when they cross 24. So, this problem is similar in principle to those that cross 12:00.

This can be shown with a 24 hour time line.

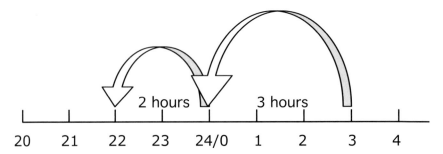

We first have to work back to the key time of 24:00 hours. This takes 3 hours.

$$5 - 3 = 2$$

There are 2 hours of the 5 hour flight left, so the smaller arrow takes us back to 22:00.

$$24:00 - 2 = 22:00$$

So the plane took off at 22:00

These methods all use subtraction in the sense of counting backwards. However, not everyone finds counting back an easy skill. If this is so, then it is possible, sometimes, to count on.

Addition and subtraction with non-time numbers, using a range of procedures is explained in detail in *"What to do when you can't add and subtract."*

Converting (changing) hours to minutes

The key fact is: There are 60 minutes in 1 hour

$$1 \text{ hour} = 60 \text{ minutes}$$

To convert from hours to minutes you multiply the number of hours by 60.

For example:

2 hours   2 x 60 = 120 minutes

5 hours   5 x 60 = 300 minutes

10 hours   10 x 60 = 600 minutes

2½ hours   2 x 60 + ½ x 60 = 120 + 30 = 150 mins

Practice

Convert these hours to minutes

a) 3 hours   ....

b) 15 hours   ....

c) 6 hours   ....

d) 12 hours   ....

e) 1½ hours   ....

f) ¼ hour   ....

g) 2 ¾ hours   ....

Answers

a) 180 min   b) 900 min   c) 360 min   d) 720 min   e) 90 min

f) 15 min   g) 165 min

Converting (changing) minutes to hours

The key fact is: There are 60 minutes in 1 hour

60 minutes = 1 hour

To convert from minutes to hours you divide the number of hours by 60.

Although this appears to be a simple reversal of the 'hours to minutes' procedure, for many people the word 'simple' may not be appropriate. Division may well be seen as more challenging than multiplication.

This perception has a reality. The procedure is more involved than the statement above suggests, mostly because only a few numbers divide exactly by 60 (for example, 120, 180, 240, 300, 600).

A further consideration is the process of division, which is often perceived as far more difficult than multiplication. This can be addressed by using key values and then adding or subtracting.

More detail of these methods can be found in *"What to do when you can't multiply and divide"*.

Key Values

1 hour	=	60 min
2 hours	=	120 min
5 hours	=	300 min
10 hours	=	600 min

For example, if you had to convert 700 minutes to hours and minutes:

Start with	700	minutes
Subtract a key value	− 600	10 hours
Minutes left	100	
Subtract a key value	− 60	1 hour
	40	min

Answer is:

10 + 1 hours and 40 minutes = 11 hours 40 minutes

Practice

Change these minutes into hours/minutes.

a) 350 minutes   ....

b) 175 minutes   ....

c) 1025 minutes   ....

d) 250 minutes   ....

e) 674 minutes   ....

Answers:-

d) 4 hours 10 minutes   e) 11 hours 14 minutes

a) 5 hours 50 min   b) 2 hours 55 minutes   c) 17 hours 5 minutes

Adding with time - minutes

Once again there is a difference compared to adding non-time numbers. The difference is down to the fact that there are 60 minutes in an hour.

Counting in minutes across an hour would be:

56 minutes, 57, 58, 59, 60 minutes which equals 1 hour, 1 hour 1 minute, 1 h 2m.

So, if I added together 52 minutes and 39 minutes:

It takes 8 minutes from the 39 minutes (leaving 31 minutes) to take 52 minutes up to 1 hour.

$$52 + 8 = 60 \text{ minutes} = 1 \text{ hour}$$

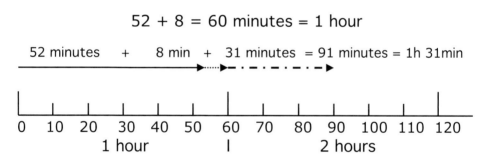

52 minutes + 39 minutes = 1 hour 31 minutes.

There is another possible way for adding minutes:

Add all the minutes: 52 + 39 = 91 minutes

Now subtract 60 minutes (1 hour): 91 – 60 = 31 minutes

52 + 39 minutes = 1 hour 31 minutes

Note: Both methods for addition involve some subtraction too.

Subtracting with time - minutes

Again, the key fact to remember is that there are 60 minutes in an hour.

An example of a subtraction:

A bus arrives at its destination at 11:55 am. The journey has taken 48 minutes. When did the bus set off?

We could present the subtraction as: 11:55 – 48 = ?

Or, to acknowledge that we are working with both hours and minutes:
$$11:55 - 00:48 = ?$$

Since the hour stays at 11, it is just a matter of subtracting the minutes:
$$55 - 48 = 7 \text{ minutes}$$

So the journey started at: 11:07 am

As a general principle, problems take time (!). Even with seemingly straightforward problems, a little forethought, putting the facts into context, thinking through the variables, finding key (easy) numbers and spotting the potential traps is the way to go.

A longer example:

A bus arrives at it destination at 12:22 pm. The journey has taken 55 minutes. When did the bus set off?

An overview of the problem should notice that the journey crosses 12 noon. Also the journey takes just under an hour (which is useful for an estimate and an alternative method).

First method

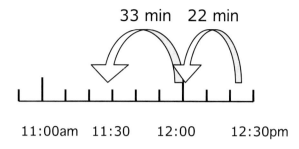

Noon has to be a focus. The first step is to ask the question:

'How many minutes to get back to noon?'

12:22 − 12:00 = 22 minutes

The next step is to ask:

'How many minutes left from the 55 minutes?'

55 − 22 = 33 minutes

Finally, the third step is to:

Subtract 33 minutes from 12:00.

This can be done directly and visually by picturing an analogue clock.

Second method

Start in the same way as in the first method by taking off the 22 minutes to get back to noon, leaving 33 minutes still to deduct.

Then subtract 30 minutes (half an hour) to reach 11:30 am and then subtract the remaining 3 minutes to reach 11:27 am.

Third method

Change 12:00 to: 11:00 and 60 minutes

so that: 12:22 becomes 11:82

55 minutes can then be subtracted.

$$82 - 55 = 27 \text{ minutes}$$

thus: 11:27 am

Fourth method

The whole question can be approached differently, by considering the 55 minutes as 5 minutes less than 1 hour.

As a first step,   12:22 – 55 minutes can be approximated to

12:22 – 60 minutes

$$12:22 - 1:00 = 11:22$$

To make the approximation an accurate answer add back 5 minutes (the difference between 1 hour and 55 minutes)

$$11:22 + 5 \text{ mins} = 11:27 \text{ am}$$

For more on alternative ways of adding and subtracting, see *"What to do when you can't add and subtract"*.

Adding with hours and minutes

First example: The added minutes do not exceed 60.

A film starts at 7:05 pm and finishes 1 hour 49 minutes later. When does it finish?

This question keeps the time change within the hour (the added minutes, 5 and 49 make 54 and are, therefore, below 60).

$$7:05 + 1 \text{ hour } 49 \text{ minutes} = 8:54 \text{ pm}$$

Second example: The added minutes cross 60 (the hour).

A film starts at 7:35 and finishes 2 hours 40 minutes later. When does it finish?

Start the process by adding the minutes:

$$35 + 40 = 75 \text{ minutes}$$

75 minutes is above 1 hour, so subtract 60 minutes to give:

$$75 - 60 = 15 \text{ minutes}$$

So 75 minutes is 1 hour and 15 minutes.

Now add the hour from the 75 minutes and the hours in the question:

$$7 + 1 + 2 = 10 \text{ pm}$$

Now bring in the 15 minutes,

$$10:00 + 00:15 \quad = \quad 10:15 \text{ pm}$$

Third example: The hours cross 12.

A film starts at 11.45pm and finishes 2 hours 10 minutes later. When does it finish?

Start by adding the minutes (checking that the total stays below 60).

$$45 + 10 = 55 \text{ minutes}$$

Now add the hours:

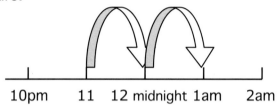

10pm   11   12 midnight 1am   2am

The hours are added in two stages:

The first 1 hour of the film takes the time from 11 pm to 12, midnight the remaining 1 hour of the 2h 10m film takes the time to 1 am

So, the film ends at: 1:55 am

Fourth example: Crossing 12 with the hours and crossing 60 with the minutes.

A film starts at 10.55pm and finishes 3 hours 12 minutes later. When does it finish?

Start with the minutes:

$$55 + 12 = 67 \text{ minutes}$$

Take away 60 minutes (1 hour):

$$67 - 60 = 7 \text{ minutes}$$
$$\text{so } 67 \text{ minutes} = 1 \text{ hour } 7 \text{ minutes}$$

Now add the 3 hours in two steps:

First add 2 hours to take 10 to 12: $10:00 + 2:00 = 12:00$

Then add the remaining hour to take the time from 12 midnight to 1:00 am.

And from adding together the minutes of the film and the time, there is another hour.

So another hour must be added to the 1:00 am.

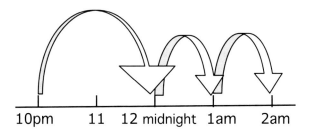

10pm   11   12 midnight 1am   2am

Putting it all together, the film ends at 2:07 am.

An alternative method

Start time: 10:55 pm.

Length of film: 3 hours 12 minutes

Add 5 minutes to 10:55:

$$10:55 + 00:05 \; = \; 11:00 \text{ pm}$$

Add 3 hours to 11:00 pm:

$$11:00 + 3 \; = \; 2:00 \text{ am}$$

Add the remaining minutes ($12 - 5 = 7$ minutes):

Finish time is: 2:07 am

The method makes use of the strategy of crossing the hour, that is making up the hour. In this case using 5 minutes from the 12 minutes to make 10:55 into 11:00 pm.

Subtracting with hours and minutes

First example: The subtracted minutes are within 60.

>A film ends at 8:54 pm.
>The film is 1 hour 49 minutes long.
>When did the film start?

This question keeps the time change within the hour (the subtracted minutes, 49, are less than the finishing time minutes, 54).

Step 1.

>Subtract the minutes: 54 – 49 = 5 minutes

Step 2.

>Subtract the hours: 8:00 pm – 1 hour = 7:00 pm

Step 3.

>Combine the answers from the two steps:
>
>>8:54 pm - 1 hour 49 minutes = 7:05 pm

Second example: The added minutes cross 60 (the hour).

>A film ends at 10:15 pm.
>The film is 1 hour 40 minutes long.
>When did the film start?

Start the process by subtracting the minutes:

$$15 - 40 = ? \text{ minutes}$$

There are not enough minutes for the subtraction, so we have to convert one of the hours into 60 minutes.

So 10:15 pm has to be converted to '9:00 pm and 75 minutes'.

Now the subtraction is: 75 – 40 = 35 minutes

Our intermediate answer is 9:35 pm, but the hour from 1 hour 40 minutes has to be subtracted:

$$9:35 - 1:00 = 8:35 \text{ pm}$$

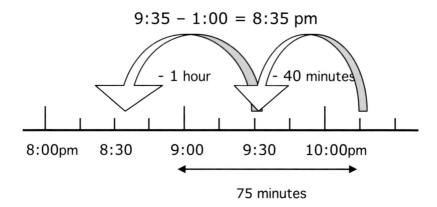

An alternative method

The film ends at 10:15 pm. It is 1 hour 40 minutes long.

Step 1.

Take away the hour: 10:15 – 1 hour = 9:15 pm

Step 2.

Separate the 40 minutes into 15 plus 25 minutes.

Step 3.

Subtract 15 minutes: 9:15 – 0:15 = 9:00 pm

Step 4.

Subtract 25 minutes from 9:00 pm

9:00 – 0:25 = 8:35 pm

Again the method separates the minutes and the hours when subtracting, dealing with each on their own.

*"What then is time? If no one asks me, I know what it is.
If I wish to explain to him who asks, I do not know."*

St Augustine

Last words

The article below was initially written for the magazine of the Association of Teachers of Mathematics. It is also used in my book, "The Trouble with Maths" (Routledge, 2004).

It was just a matter of time

Old Dr Algy B'rah faced the Lower Third maths class for lesson 10 on Friday afternoon.....

"Now, today, or perhaps it was yesterday, when I said it would be tomorrow. In fact sometime recently I said that it was about time I spent some time teaching you time.

Time is easy to understand and to help I've brought in a real clock. This is the clock face. You'll see that it doesn't have eyes or a nose but it does have hands. Unlike you there are three hands to one face. The first hand is an hour, not the our as in 'your' hand; the second hand is the minute hand and the third hand is the second hand. Is that clear?

The little hand is the hour hand and the big hand is the minute hand. That's minute not mi-nute, otherwise it wouldn't be big would it?

There are numbers round the clock face. They start with 1, which is not the number at the top and go round to 12 which is at the top. This is because there are 24 hours in a day. So there are 24 hours in a day and we put 12 of them on a clock and use them twice.

Now see all these little marks. They are the marks for minutes which can also be used for seconds and there are 60 of those, so 1 means 1 if it's hours and 5 if it's minutes and 5 if it's seconds and 2 means 10 minutes when it's not hours and 10 seconds when it's not minutes.

So there are 60 minutes in an hour and 60 seconds in a minute and we only use them once, not twice like hours.

When the big hand is pointing at 12 and the little hand is pointing at 4 it is four o'clock. No it isn't really 4 o'clock now, sit down, and no, Seamus, o'clock is not an Irish name.

The hands go round and round and round. It is all very logical. It takes the hour hand half a day to go round. It takes the minute hand an hour to go round and it takes the second hand a minute to go round. And when the hour hand has been round twice it's tomorrow and today becomes yesterday.

Now, when we start to go past o'clock, we get to times like 5 past 1, which we write the other way round as 1.05. This means the little hand starts to move away from the 1 and the big, minute hand moves away from the 12. The little hand heads for 2 and the big, minute hand moves away from the 12, which also means zero, but it doesn't say it, and heads for the 1 which also means 5. This goes until 30 minutes past 1, which is also half past 1, which is also 1.30, but the '.' is not a decimal and 30 is not the decimal .30 which would be $3/10$, but now it's ½, not the half that is also .50, so we have to remember that ½ can be written as .30, but if you do that with decimal numbers I will mark it wrong.

Then we say 25 'to 2', which is not tutu or to to or two two and 20 to 2 and quarter to 2 and 10 to 2. Of course 20 to 2 could be one third to 2, but that would be difficult so we don't say that, because we want time to be easy. And of course 20 to 2 could be one forty, which is not the same as forty one backwards, because we always say the hour first except when we say it second after the minutes. And the to is not two or 10 to 2 would be 1022 which is forty four years before the Battle of Hastings.

So we count up in minutes after the hour, but only until 30 minutes after the hour, then we count down to the next hour, even though the minute hand is now moving up, except when we use times like 1.35. This means we change the hour we are talking about at half past the first hour and use the next hour half an hour before we reach the next hour. Once you think about that it all becomes clear, doesn't it?

Now you have all that clear we can move on to the 24 hour clock which is used for trains, buses and aeroplanes, all examples where you really need to know time to be on time. We still use the 12 hour clock face I've shown you but when we go round the second time with the hour hand we now have to remember that for the 24 hour clock 1 means 13, 2 is 14, 3 is 15 and so on. So the 1 on the clock face can mean 1 for hours, 13 for hours, 5 for minutes and 5 for seconds. When we get past 6 numbers like 9 can mean 9, 21, 45 or 1/4 and 7 can mean 7, 19, 35 or 25. And don't forget that $10 + 5 = 3$ with the 12 hour clock and $10 + 5 = 15$ with the 24 hour clock and $23 + 8 = 07$ with the 24 hour clock and I know we haven't written 0 in front of a whole number before.

On the 24 hour clock after times like fifteen fifty nine we go to sixteen hundred, which is really fifteen sixty, but after 59 we go back to zero again and call it hundred. This means we have to remember again that 20.40 is still not the same as 20.40 in decimals but is the same as 8.40 and 20 to 9. That's clear to me, so it should be clear to you.

I just can't understand why you can't do time. No I don't mean 'do time' as in 'doing time' Bodger."

And we expect young children to understand time!

Learners who are insecure or uncertain do not handle inconsistencies well. Time is full of inconsistencies, in the vocabulary used and in the way numbers are used.

More practice

Convert these digital times to ' ____ minutes to ____ '

For example,

8:35 will be '25 to 9'

1) **07:44** _____ to _____

2) **11:52** _____ to _____

3) **09:37** _____ to _____

4) **10:41** _____ to _____

Convert these analogue times to digital times

a) A journey starts at 5 pm and takes 4 hours.
When do you arrive? ....

b) A journey starts at 4:30 am and takes 6 hours.
At what 'am' time do you arrive? ....

c) A journey starts at 10:00 am and takes 6 hours.
At what 'pm' time do you arrive? ....

d) A journey starts at 11:15 am and takes 4 hours.
At what 'pm' time do you arrive? ....

e) A plane takes off at 15:00 and lands 6 hours later. At what time does it land? ....

f) A plane takes off at 20:00 and lands 8 hours later. At what time does it land? ....

g) A plane takes off at 18:00 and lands 5 hours later. At what time does it land? ....

i) A plane takes off at 19:20 and lands 10 hours later. At what time does it land? ....

Answers:-

h) 05:20   g) 23:00   f) 04:00   e) 21:00
d) 3.15 pm   c) 4 pm   b) 10.30 am   a) 9 pm
1) 16 mins to 8 2) 8 mins to 12 3) 23 mins to 10 4) 19 mins to 11

Blank Clocks

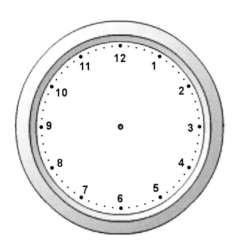

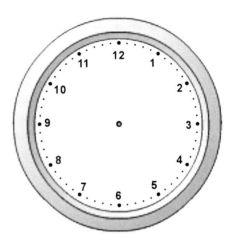

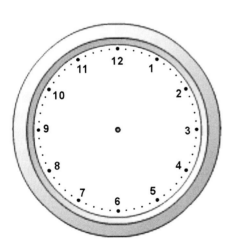

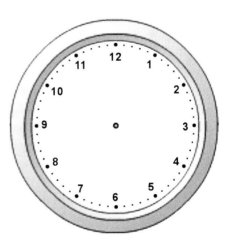